Childhood Days

in pictures

For Alice and her Grandad

Pictures
to share

First published in 2011 by
Pictures to Share Community Interest Company,
a UK based social enterprise that publishes
illustrated books for older people.

www.picturestoshare.co.uk

ISBN 978-0-9563818-2-8

Front Cover: Smiling little girl © Hélène Desplechin 2009 / Flickr Select/Getty Images
Endpapers: The Princess and the Pea © Ann Bridges. www.ann-bridges.com
Title page: 'Euan' © Helen Bate
Back cover: Detail from Boys finding treasure Page 23
Detail from Girls in sea. Page 25
Detail from Girl with tadpoles. Page 27

Childhood Days
in pictures

Edited by Helen J Bate

Golden slumbers
kiss your eyes,
Smiles await you
when you rise.

Sleep, pretty baby,
Do not cry,
And I will sing
a lullaby.

Quotation from Cradle Song by Thomas Dekker (1572 - 1632)
a poem used by the Beatles as the inspiration for their 'Cradle Song'
on the 1969 Abbey Road album.

Photograph: New born baby swaddled.

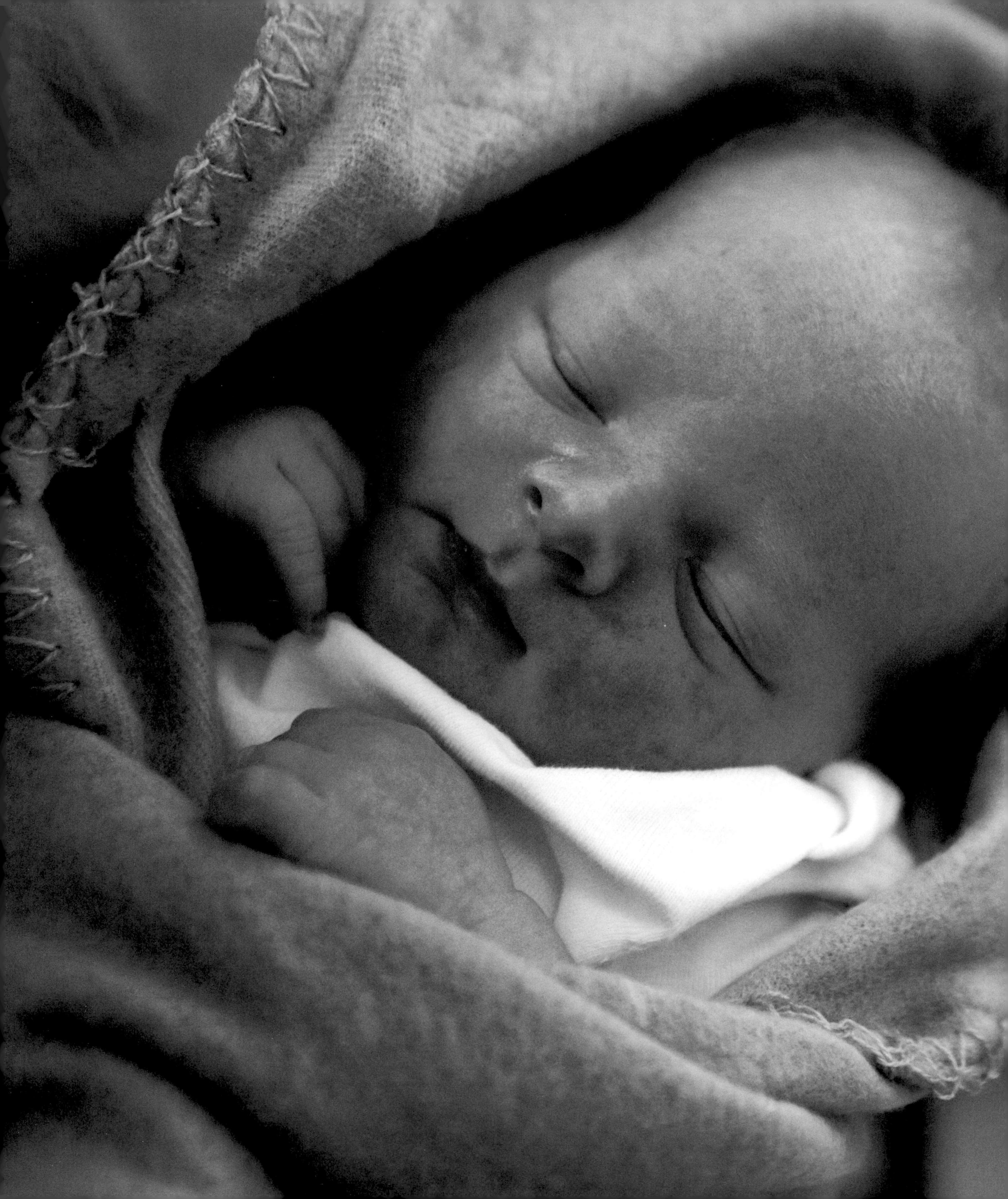

Kookaburra sits in the old gum tree,

Merry merry king of the bush is he.

Laugh, Kookaburra,
laugh, Kookaburra,
Gay your life must be!

Quotation: A popular Australian nursery rhyme and round about the Kookaburra (an Australian bird), written by Marion Sinclair (1895–1988).

Main and small photograph: Christmas carols at St Clements Danes School, Drury Lane. 1926. © UPPA/Photoshot

What are little boys made of?

What are little boys made of?
Frogs and snails
And puppy-dogs' tails,
That's what little boys are made of.

What are little girls made of?
What are little girls made of?
Sugar and spice
And all that's nice,
That's what litle girls are made of.

Quotation: Traditional nursery rhyme
Photograph: © UPPA/Photoshot

What is this life if, full of care,

We have no time to stand and stare?

No time to stand beneath the boughs,
And stare as long as sheep and cows;

No time to see, when woods we pass,
Where squirrels hide their nuts in grass;

A poor life this if, full of care,
We have no time to stand and stare.

Quotation from Leisure by W.H.Davies
(1871 – 1940) a Welsh poet and writer.

Painting: On the Plain by Karl Fredrick Nordstrom

I kissed my first girl

and smoked my first cigarette
on the same day.

I haven't had time
for tobacco since.

Quotation: Arturo Toscanini
Italian virtuoso Conductor (1867 - 1957)

Main photograph: A Romany boy smoking.

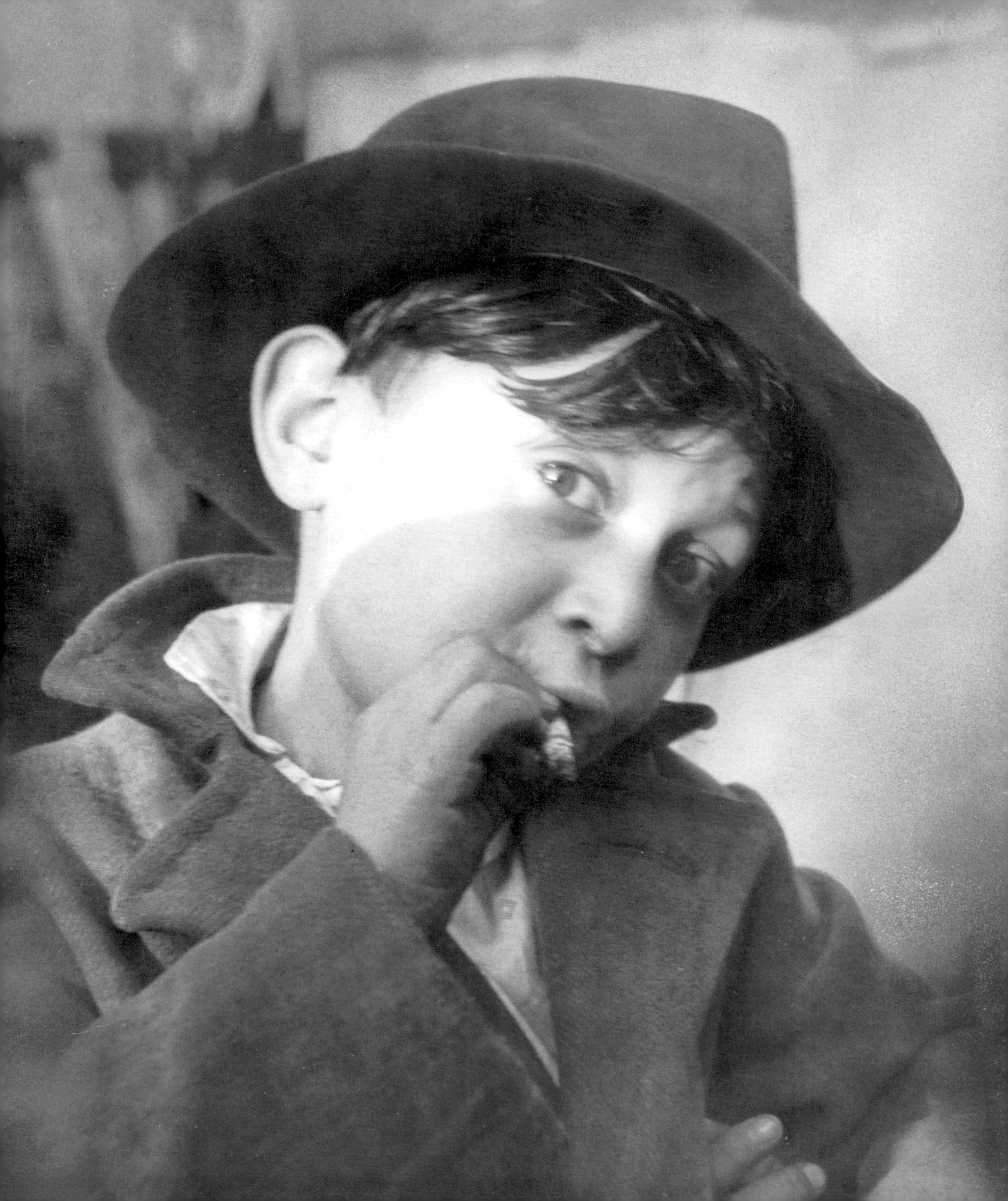

Daisy, Daisy,

Give me your answer do
I'm half crazy,
All for the love of you
It won't be a stylish marriage,
I can't afford a carriage,
But you'll look sweet upon the seat
Of a bicycle built for two

Quotation: Words from song 'Daisy Bell'
(A Bicycle Built for Two) by Harry Dacre, 1892

Main photograph: Child with long daisy chain
(Bellis perennis) on lawn in spring.

Small photograph:

Courage

is being scared to death...
and saddling up anyway.

Quotation: John Wayne, American Actor

Photograph: Boy dressed as cowboy.

Two little dickie birds sitting on a wall
One named Peter one named Paul

Fly away Peter

Fly away Paul
Come back Peter
Come back Paul

Quotation: From 'Two Little Dickie Birds'
An English Nursery Rhyme and Finger Play.

Main photograph: Young boy with bird on hand.

Small photograph: Detail from above.

Summer afternoon.

To me
those have always been
the two most beautiful words
in the English language.

Quotation: Henry James (1843 - 1916)
Quoted in Edith Wharton 'A Backward Glance' (1934)

Photograph: A mother cycles off with her young toddler on the passenger seat of her bicycle.

If I had influence with the good fairy

I should ask that her gift
to each child in the world
be a sense of wonder
so indestructible
that it would last throughout life.

Quotation: Rachel Carson (1907 - 1964)
American biologist and conservationist

Main photograph: Boys finding treasure in the hole of a tree.

Small photograph: Wood Mouse

To the outside world we all grow old.

But not to brothers and sisters.

We know each other
as we always were.

We live outside the touch of time.

Quotation: Clara Ortega
www.searchquotes.com

Main photograph: © UPPA/Photoshot

A frog he would a-wooing go,

Hey ho, says Rowley,
A frog he would a-wooing go,
Whether his mother would let him or no.
With a rowley, powley, gammon and spinach,
Hey ho, says Anthony Rowley.

Quotation: from Traditional Nursery Rhyme

Main photograph: Young girl looking at tadpoles.

Small photograph: Frog

The School Milk Act

was passed by the
UK Government in 1946.

This act ordered the issue
of one-third of a pint of milk
free to all pupils
under eighteen.

Photograph: One of the four 'Good' quadruplets
enjoying her milk at Westerleigh School. Picture Post pub. 1953

Away in a manger,

No crib for His bed
The little Lord Jesus
Laid down His sweet head.

The stars in the bright sky
Looked down where He lay,
The little Lord Jesus
Asleep on the hay.

Quotation: Traditional children's Christmas Carol first published in 1885

Painting: Foundling Girls at Prayer in the Chapel, c.1877
by Sophie Gengembre Anderson (1823 – 1903) a French-born British artist.
Owned by the Coram Family in the care of the Foundling Museum,
London/The Bridgeman Art Library, Getty Images.

Pennies don’t fall from heaven.

They have to be earned here on earth.

Quotation: Baroness Margaret Thatcher (1925 -)
quoted in the Observer 'Sayings of the Week' 18th Nov. 1979

Main photograph: A little child helps her parents wash the family car. © Raymond Kleboe/Hulton Archive/Getty Images

LPG 942

This little pig went to market,

This little pig stayed at home.

Quotation: Traditional children's rhyme

Main photograph: Two girls with pig.

Small photograph:

Our Father

which art in heaven,
Hallowed be thy name.

Thy kingdom come.
Thy will be done on earth,
as it is in heaven.

Give us this day our daily bread.
And forgive us our trespasses,
as we forgive those
who trespass against us.

And lead us not into temptation,
but deliver us from evil:

For thine is the kingdom,
the power, and the glory,
forever and ever.

Amen.

Text: The Lord's prayer

Photograph: Two of the 5 year old 'Good' quadruplets saying their prayers at school

Winning may not be everything,

but losing has little
to recommend it.

Quotation: Senator Dianne Feinstein US Democratic politician (1933 -)

Main photograph: The game of Lotto, 1865 (oil on canvas)
Charles Joshua Chaplin (1825 – 1891) French painter and engraver.

We don't make mistakes,

we make happy accidents.

Quotation: Bob Ross, "The Joy of Painting with Bob Ross" PBS.
American Artist and TV Presenter (1942 - 1995)

Main photograph: young painter at the new Bousfield Primary School, Kensington, London. © Folb/Hulton Archive/Getty Images
Handprint: © Nito100/istockphoto

car
The days of the we
Monday
Tuesday
Wednesday
Thursday
Friday
Saturday
Sunday

Music notation from 'Home on the Range' Traditional American song
Main photograph: © _snark_/istockphoto

The cure for boredom is curiosity.

There is no cure for curiosity.

Quotation: Dorothy Parker, (attributed)
US author, humourist, poet, & wit (1893 - 1967)

Photograph: Chairmaker at work

We will travel as far as we can,

but we cannot in one lifetime
see all that we would like to see,
or learn all that we hunger to know.

Quotation: Loren Eiseley. American anthropologist, educator and philosopher (1907 - 1977)

Main photograph: A young girl sleeping in a railway carriage after an exhausting day at the seaside
© Haywood Magee/Hulton Archive/Getty Images
Small photograph: Model train © Andrew Howe istockphoto

Acknowledgements
Our thanks to the contributors who have allowed their imagery to be used for a reduced or no fee.

Thanks to our sponsors

Published by
Pictures to Share Community Interest Company
Tattenhall, Cheshire
www.picturestoshare.co.uk

Printed in England by
BPC Ltd, 4 Burlington Park,
High Street, Foxton, CB22 6SA

"They knew that she was a real princess because she had felt the pea through twenty mattresses"